MIDDLE AGES

Brian Moses is a poet, editor and percussionist who lives on the Sussex coast with his wife and two daughters. He travels the country presenting his poems in schools and libraries. His knowledge of history is extensive and he can say that almost everything you read in this book might well have been true!

Mike Phillips is big, bald and blooming good fun. He lives in Essex with his wife and three children, illustrating books from his garden shed.

Also available from Macmillan

Hysterical HISTORICAL Poems

MIDDLE AGES

Chosen by Brian Moses

Illustrated by Mike Phillips

MACMILLAN CHILDREN'S BOOKS

First published 2000
by Macmillan Children's Books
a division of Macmillan Publishers Ltd
25 Eccleston Place, London SW1W 9NF
Basingstoke and Oxford
www.macmillan.co.uk

Associated companies throughout the world

ISBN 0 330 37714 0

1 3 5 7 9 8 6 4 2

A CIP catalogue record for this book is available from the British Library.

Printed by Mackays of Chatham plc, Chatham, Kent.

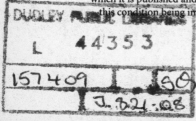

Contents

Entry from King Canute's Diary

August 4th 1027

Took courtiers to seaside for a treat.
Ate bacon sandwiches on beach. Sea air
gave One an appetite. Relaxed in deckchair.
Courtiers sure would be OK. Dozed off.
High tide 2.30. Socks v. wet. Still,
courtiers didn't let One drown, so
must be pretty popular!

Sue Cowling

The King Who Got His Feet Wet

When people tell you
you can't fail, and flatter
you with smiling lies,

the best thing yet
is to remember
the King who got his feet wet.

And when they say
you are the strongest, and
you can't do any wrong,

the best thing yet
is to remember
the King who got his feet wet.

His name was Canute
and in order to refute
the views of those who thought
his the most powerful court,
he sat upon a pebbly beach
and waited for the water to reach
his most royal toes
in order to show
that even he
couldn't stop the sea.

The King Who Got His Feet Wet

So, if you ever feel
you could beat the world ...

the best thing yet
is to remember
the King who got his feet wet.

Robin Mellor

William the Conqueror Sends a Postcard Home

Hastings 14th Oct 1066

Dear Mum,

Having a lovely time in England.
Arrived at Pevensey but the beach was rubbish.
Moved to Battle – and guess what?
Had a battle there (ho ho)
Harold turned up late (typically British)
So we chose to defend the hill (clever move)
Not much luck with horses (three killed!)
Men needed to know I was alive, so
Fought without helmet.
(I know I promised to wear it all the time)
We pretended to run away (very clever)
The English chased us (very stupid)
Result – One nil to the Normans.
Guess what? I have a new nickname.
William the Conqueror (good eh?)
Weather fine … Wish you were here.
Your loving son,
William (King of England!)
P.S. England is now back to Norman (ho! ho! ho!)

John Coldwell

William the Conqueror, 1066

They didn't have the radio,
they didn't have TV,
so they stitched the Bayeux Tapestry
for everyone to see.
Even now in modern times,
these medieval pix
tell the fate of Harold in
AD 1066
when scheming William stormed defences,
eager for the Crown,
and the English hacked with battleaxes,
mowing Normans down,
and Normans fired arrows, raining
death down from the sky
striking Harold (legend has it)
smack bang, in the eye.
That's how the Normans conquered
and the Anglo Saxons fled
leaving Harold lying there,
very very dead,
and in Bayeux, in Normandy,
the women, filled with glee,
stitched the Bayeux tapestry
for everyone to see.

Marian Swinger

A Lesson in Conquering

William the Conqueror
With his Norman band
Rode around England
Grabbing all the land.

He ransacked Saxon villages
And set fire to their wheat,
He pillaged and he plundered,
He cut off hands and feet.

He chopped the heads off rebels
Or hung them by their thumbs,
He slaughtered cows and pigs and sheep
And frightened timid nuns.

Then when it was all over
And he had a lot less worry,
He built some lovely churches
To show that he was sorry.

Patricia Leighton

Neighbourhood Witch Patrol

Watch for warts
or creepy black cats.
Watch for someone
talking to bats
or frogs
or even to their brooms.
Watch for a face
as ugly as doom.

When you catch your witch,
take her down to the river.
Here's one simple test
you can easily give her:
    add weights to arms
    add weights to feet;
    then throw in your witch,
    where the river is fleet.

If your warty witch floats,
then you've got one to burn.
If the witch drowns . . . Well,
let's say, that's one way to learn.

Watch for warts
or creepy black cats.
Watch for someone
talking to bats.

Mike Johnson

Safe at Castle

Portcullis down, drawbridge up,
safe against attacks.
The serfs have all been soundly whipped
and shiver in their shacks.
'Good,' sighs Sir Percy
'time to relax.'

A kitchen-boy turns the heavy spit,
the cook hurls pots at mice.
Before the great hall's roaring fire
the dogs scratch at their lice.
'Mm,' hums Sir Percy,
'isn't this nice.'

An owl hoots on the battlements
the winter wind makes moan
and in the pit beneath his keep
the starving prisoners groan.
'Ah,' sighs Sir Percy,
'there's no place like home.'

Dave Calder

Rules of the Castle Hotel

**(N.B. If a motel is especially for motorists then it
follows that a hotel is for those who ride horses)**

The following requests
Are made to our hotel guests.

Please do not take your horse to your room
But leave it in the stable with our groom.

Please do not duel or joust in the hotel grounds.
When dining, please do not throw your bones to the hounds.

Forks are available for those who wish to try this new
    invention.
If you are not sure how to use one, the serving maids will be
    pleased to give a demonstration.

The armour in the hall
And the shields on the wall
Are ONLY for display
And are not to be used in any other way.

Kindly dispose of all water down the spillway
In your room. Please do not throw it away
Out the window.

The drawbridge is raised each eve at half past ten.
If you are returning later, then
You may use a boat
to cross the moat.
We hope that you enjoy your stay.
(Dungeon accommodation is available for those who do
    not pay!)

Alan Priestley

At the Pilgrim Shrine

Holy bones, holy bones,
the things they liked best
were holy bones.

There were nicknacks
and trinkets galore on display,
cheap wooden crosses
and saints made of clay.

But holy bones, holy bones,
the things they liked best
were holy bones.

They laughed at felt hats
saying *Kisseth Me Quick*
they carved hearts on stone,
and *Elspeth Loves Dick.*

But holy bones, holy bones,
the things they liked best
were holy bones.

Bits of saints' fingernails,
shrivelled-up thumbs,
a martyr's skin stretched
on a heathen's drum.

Skulls and boiled thigh bones,
hair of Saint John,
wood from the wheel
they spun Catherine on.

Pilgrims rich, pilgrims poor,
seeking magical mysteries –
miracles – cures –

from bones, bones
holy bones,
That's what they came for
Holy bones.

Patricia Leighton

The Perils of Armour

I am a knight.
I've lost my shield.
I've fallen off my horse
in the middle of a field.

I'm on my back.
My arms clank about.
My visor's down:
no one hears me shout.

All I can see
are the clouds in the sky.
I'm hoping for a helpful
passer-by.

If no one travels
this way, I fear
I'll be stuck like this
for the rest of the year.

Charles Thomson

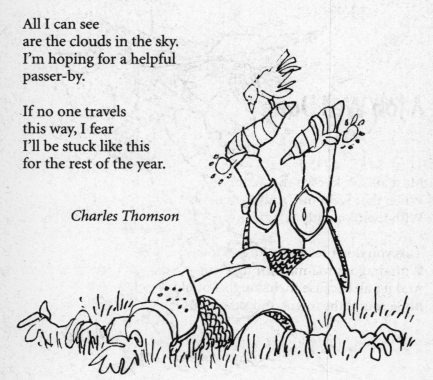

A Job Well Done

Them Medieval knights of old
Must all 'ave known their stuff
When they went out 'unting dragons
With their knightly 'uff an' puff.

'Cos you don't see many streets today
With dragons roamin' through 'em –
And it's all because them knights of old
Rode round the towns and slew 'em!

Clive Webster

To the Gauntlet Knight Hiring Service

Dear Sir,

I feel I must complain,
Your service must be slacking
Do you suppose I'm happy with
A knight who is so lacking?

I did expect, when he arrived,
I'd find inside the armour
a handsome, dashing man of youth,
A romantic little charmer!

Your advert states that you supply
Knights – daring, brave and bold;
Mine may have been in days gone
But now he's rather old.

You promise chivalry and strength
You claim your knights have flair,
But I'd have been quite happy with
A knight with teeth and hair!

And so I must return to you,
Inside this hempen sack,
A knight who has seen many days –
I WANT MY MONEY BACK!!
                    Sent Chain Mail

                              Coral Rumble

Sir Guy Is In His Keep Tonight

The twelfth of December 1231
terrible snows, darkness, no sun
the castle is cold, silent and grey
I'm here on my own
my wife and children far away
on a winter holiday.
I've spent all the morning jousting
knocking knights off their horses
then archery in the butts, some swordplay
but I'm on my own tonight, of course
I've got all my servants and soldiers
the fires burning bright
but I'm alone in the keep
on my own
tonight.

I can see them clearly
swarming over the curtain wall
flooding the inner bailey
the thousand ghosts of the thousand Saxons
my father and his father
slaughtered daily
the Saxons fought well, died hard
look at them cover the castle's yard
ghosts, grey in the moonlight
bearded warriors of yesterday
coming for me
tonight.

David Harmer

A Letter from Lady Eleanor to her Husband, Sir Edgar

Dear Sir Edgar,

When you rode to a battle you looked a most handsome sight.
A fine figure of a man – a worthy knight.
I was relieved to see you so well protected.
That pear-shaped shield over which just your head projected
Should fend off the arrows designed to hurt
And those that do
get through
will merely rattle against your chain mail shirt.
Your helmet will deflect the hacks of any axe
And your nose guard will keep your fine
face safe from attacks, smacks and whacks.

But when you return victorious, all hot and dusty,
Don't bathe in your shirt or you might go rusty.

With my deepest love,

Lady Eleanor

John Coldwell

Roger Bacon, c.1214–1292

They laughed till they ached.
The things he said!
The events he predicted!
Quite off his head.

That wagons would roll
At tremendous speed
Without ox or horse!
They all tee-heed.

That ocean ships
Would voyage out
Without sail or oar!
They fell about.

That a boat could visit
The ocean floor
With people inside!
They roared and roared.

That men would be lifted
Into the skies
And fly like birds!
They split their sides.

In his *Opus Magus*
He wrote these things down
Regardless of them.
Who's laughing now?

Frances Nagle

Conversation with a Spider

'Call yourself King of the Scots!' said the spider.
'Hiding here in this filthy farm shed.
Look at you: ragged and wretched.'
'I've given up hope,' the king said.

'Take me now,' the spider went on,
'My web: wrecked six times this last week.
Did I bury my head in my legs and lose hope?'
'Do you mind,' said the king, 'if I speak?

'After that battle at Dalry
The outlook is blacker than black.
My army was totally smashed by the English.
I just can't see any way back.

'My three brothers were all executed.
God knows what's become of my wife.
Do you wonder I'm slightly downhearted?
I barely escaped with my life.'

'Don't think I'm not sympathetic,'
Said the spider, 'about your near squeak.
But to get back to what I was saying
About all those repair jobs last week.

'Six times I wept over the wreckage.
But did I give up on it? No—!'
'OK,' said the king, 'got your message.
I'll give it another go.'

[To discover how Robert the Bruce
Made his own luck, and Scotland's luck, turn:
Just get down that big history book
And look up the name *Bannockburn*.]

Eric Finney

Third Time Lucky

You're feeling a failure?
Your life is no use?
I'll tell you the tale
Of King Robert the Bruce.

The enemy English
Had beaten him TWICE,
He was blinded by failure
And deaf to advice.
He hid in a cave
Like a thief on the run
He shielded his shame
From the glare of the sun
While over the doorway,
Like shrouds for the dead,
A spider was weaving
Its silvery thread.

The king watched in silence
As Scottish gales blew
Tearing the Web,
Like his future, in two.
Yet the spider, unshocked
By the wind and the rain,
Climbed up the wall
And just started again.
No sooner was Web
Number Two all complete
When along came a storm
And a second defeat.

Did that spider give up
And sob, 'Poor little me'?
It simply began to spin
Web Number Three.
So Robert the Bruce
Raised his sword in the air,
Crying, 'Hello to Courage,
Goodbye to Despair.'
He charged off to conquer
The English, my friend,
Inspired by a spider
To win in the end.

So don't be a loser,
Forget your excuse –
Remember the story
Of Robert the Bruce.

Clare Bevan

The Dark Ages

Miss Trilby says, in ancient days
the lights went out – all black as crypts;
the monks hit on this brilliant craze –
illuminating manuscripts.

Mina Johnson

Football Violence

Village football,
Dirty knees –
The ball's a pig's bladder
Stuffed with peas.

No football lessons
At football schools;
No red cards.
There are no rules.

All the men took part.
The pitch was filled.
Many players were hurt
And some were killed.

But King Edward the Third
Saddened the land
When he decreed
That the game be banned.

John Kitching

Praise Be!

A happy monk called Basil
Loved his peaceful little cell,
The tasty fish on Fridays
And the beer and wine as well.

He loved the quiet chats he had
With brother monks each day
And working in the gardens
With no worries about pay.

'O, thank you, Lord,' said Basil,
'For keeping me from strife.
I might have had ten children
And one
      nagging
         wife!'

Patricia Leighton

Miracle Cures

Headache? Backache? Earache? Sick?
Dr Quack can heal you – quick.

Kiss these saintly sacred relics,
drink this drop of herbal mix;
lay a leech beneath your tongue,
atop your head drop chicken dung.
Wrap both feet in warm intestines;
Dr Quack has ways and means,
of curing every kind of trouble
(for fevers, doc doth charge you double).
Evil plagues are kept away,
by sprinkling toad's spawn in sour whey,
but sleep not facing to the West;
smear rancid pig grease round your chest,
then splash green stagnant water on.
Soon, every ache and pain is gone.
'These remedies shalt cure thy lack
of health and strength,' sayeth Dr Quack.

Headache? Backache? Earache? Sick?
Dr Quack can heal you – quick.

Mike Johnson

A Royal Roar of Approval

Medical transplants AREN'T so new!

They happened LONG ago!

King Richard had a lion's heart.

(I just thought you'd like to know …!)

Trevor Harvey

Joan of Arc

All the girls I've ever met
(Plus myself, of course,)
Want to be like Joan of Arc –
A hero on a horse.

Want to hear a secret voice,
Want to lead the men,
Want to ride past castle walls
And then ride back again.

Want to wear our hair cut short
Want our mums to faint,
Want to look like Joan of Arc
And turn into a Saint.

Want the fame without the flames
(Grilling girls is rotten,)
Want to LIVE like Joan of Arc
And NEVER be forgotten.

Clare Bevan

All Our Jesterdays

Having a party?
Why not hire a
jester for the day?

Our jesters arrive at your front door
in motley garb, including cap of bells,
to set you and your friends laughing.
Giggle with joy as he dances, capers
and tumbles across your living room.
His jokes and puns will have even
the glummest guest guffawing.
Is our jester a witty fool or a foolish wit?
A clever remark on any subject – guaranteed
But don't take our word for it.
Let you and your guests put him to the test.

(In the unlikely event of our jesters
not proving to be amusing
you may place them in the stocks
and pelt them with the rotten fruit of your choice.)

So what are you waiting for?
Call All Our Jesterdays now!

John Coldwell

The Peasants' Revolt, 1381

There was a grumbling in the land
and soon the peasants were revolting.
    In their hordes they massed for battle
    but, alas, smelled just like cattle.
    Most were dandruffy and toothless
    as in rags they fought the ruthless.
    The poor peasants, pock-marked, potty,
    were all scabby-legged and spotty.
They came in cartloads, sick with jolting.
Oh yes,
the peasants were revolting.

There was a mumbling in the land
and soon the peasants were revolting.
    Armed with scythes and pitchforks (rusty),
    they were dirty, drunk and dusty.
    Grimy hands hurled stones and boulders.
    Nitty hair hung to their shoulders.
    The sad peasants, squint-eyed, shabby,
    were as thin as rakes, or flabby.
Their goatskin coats were patched, some moulting.
Oh yes,
    the peasants were revolting.

Wes Magee

What the King Said to Wat Tyler

You peasants are quite revolting,

Go away and come back in an hour.

We cannot discuss your demands

Until you've all had a shower.

John Foster

Fourteenth Scentury High Street Tour

'Good people, pray may I have your attention. My name's Will and I'm your Past Century's tour guide. May I start by welcoming you to my fourteenth scentury high street. In today's walk I will waft you through the stamping ground of medieval citizens of the commonest rank. Do stay close and you won't get lost – as the folks round here say, "where there's Will there's the way!"

Now, the first thing you'll notice is the homely smell – we don't call this our high street for nothing! We locals are used to it, but if there's too much atmosphere for you, do help yourself to a nosegay specially imported from our olfactory in the countryside.

Let me start by drawing your attention to *Ye Olde Butcher's Shoppe* on our left. As you can see, ye olde butcher has hung his carcasses out to ripen to tenderness. Mmmmm – imagine a nice piece of ye olde English tenderloin with boiled cabbage on the side – delicious! By the way, see that ditch in front of the butcher's, now you know why it became known as a gutter.

Now, the leaning hovel we're about to pass under belongs to Master Scales our fishmonger. Do beware as you pass by as every day at about this hour the Master's lady whiff disposes of her rubbish from that window into the street. LOOK OUT! – Oh dear, I did warn you. Not to worry – soak your costumes overnight in stale urine and those stains will come out a treat.

Now, that alley on the right is what I call our public relief road. If anyone's desperate now's your chance! Ah – now, from this stile if you look over yonder, next to the yard where the tanner is scraping his skins, you will catch your first glimpse of my humble home sweet home.

What's that folks – you've "seen" enough and wish to leave the tour immediately? It's funny that. I wonder why our fourteenth scentury tour never makes it beyond the stile by the high street cesspit?'

Philip Waddell

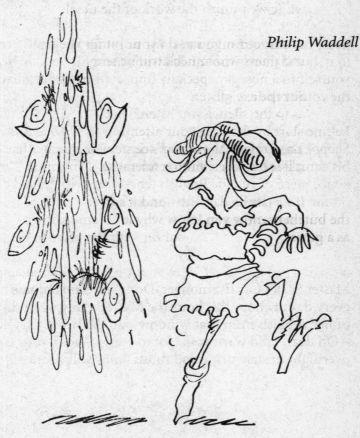

A Family Outing

It's a great day out —
a chance for the children to scream and shout.

It's a family treat —
they'll love that special drum beat.

A chance for you to revel
while we punish the work of the devil.

A chance for you to do your bit for the law
and guess whose neck will be sore.

See the axe glisten
as to the silence you listen.

Then finally the crowd's deafening roar —
it'll leave you shouting for more.

It's a family day out — and it's free:
a day at the exe

                cution — it's the place to be.

Tim Pointon

I Love the Middle Ages

Ducking stools and witches
people stuck in stocks,
millers in their windmills
kings in funny socks . . .
torturing and castles
wimples, knives and knights
chopping blocks and axes
tons and tons of fights!

Yes . . . bring back the Middle Ages
put teachers in the stocks
put grown-ups in the dungeons
and lock up all the locks
let children be the barons
let children have the wine
and holidays for ever
in – NEW
    Middle Ages
     Time.

Peter Dixon

Career Opportunity: Knight Required

Are you brave, honourable
and chivalrous?
Do you like wearing metal suits
and enjoy being called Sir?
Then this could be the job for you.

Your duties will include
wielding a sword, jousting
and clanking about.

Preference will be given
to those candidates
who come equipped
with their own warhorse and squire.

If you think
you've got what it takes,
turn up for an interview
and show us what you can do.

NB Candidates will be left
to fight it out amongst themselves.
Castle Management accepts no responsibility
for loss of life or limb.

Bernard Young